NEW
ROCK
ANTHEMS
GUITAR

© 2006 BY FABER MUSIC LTD
FIRST PUBLISHED BY FABER MUSIC LTD IN 2006
3 QUEEN SQUARE, LONDON WC1N 3AU

TOM FLEMING (GUITARS)
NEIL WILLIAMS (BASS)
DARRIN MOONEY (DRUMS)
SEAN HARGREAVES & TOM FLEMING (KEYBOARDS)
ALISON SYMONS & JO EDWARDS (BACKING VOCALS)

RECORDED AT THE MEWS RECORDING STUDIOS, LONDON
DAVE CLARKE (RECORDING AND MIX ENGINEER)
WWW.THEMEWSRECORDINGSTUDIOS.COM

ARRANGED & ENGRAVED BY TOM FLEMING
COMPILED BY LUCY HOLLIDAY
EDITED BY LUCY HOLLIDAY & OLLY WEEKS
DESIGNED BY DOMINIC BROOKMAN & LYDIA MERRILLS-ASHCROFT
PHOTOGRAPHS FROM REDFERNS MUSIC PICTURE LIBRARY

PRINTED IN ENGLAND BY CALIGRAVING LTD
ALL RIGHTS RESERVED

ISBN 0-571-52523-7

REPRODUCING THIS MUSIC IN ANY FORM IS ILLEGAL AND FORBIDDEN BY
THE COPYRIGHT, DESIGNS AND PATENTS ACT, 1988

TO BUY FABER MUSIC PUBLICATIONS
OR TO FIND OUT ABOUT THE FULL RANGE OF TITLES AVAILABLE,
PLEASE CONTACT YOUR LOCAL MUSIC RETAILER OR FABER MUSIC SALES ENQUIRIES:

FABER MUSIC LTD, BURNT MILL, ELIZABETH WAY, HARLOW, CM20 2HX ENGLAND
TEL: +44(0)1279 82 89 82 FAX: +44(0)1279 82 89 83
SALES@FABERMUSIC.COM FABERMUSIC.COM

I BET YOU LOOK GOOD ON THE DANCEFLOOR

WORDS AND MUSIC BY ALEX TURNER

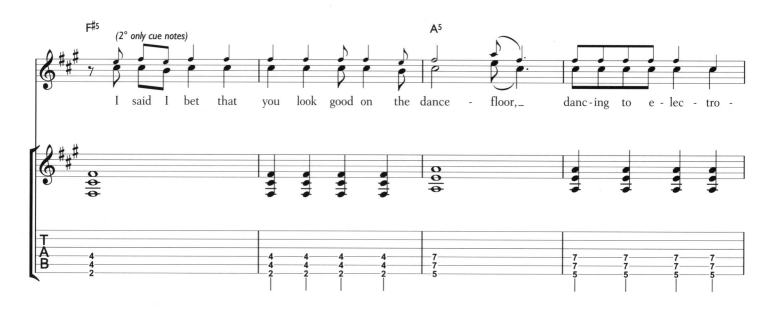

I said I bet that you look good on the dance - floor,_ danc-ing to e - lec - tro -

-pop like a ro - bot from nine - teen-eigh - ty - four,_ well from nine - teen eigh - ty -

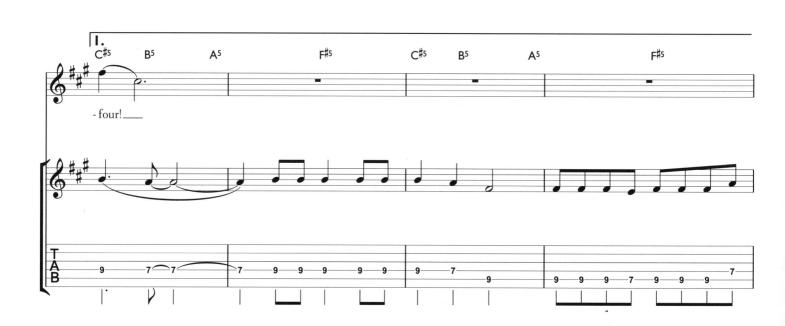

-four!___

and   dir - ty dance - floors___   and dreams of naugh - ti - ness!

FORGET MYSELF

WORDS BY GUY GARVEY
MUSIC BY ELBOW

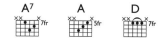

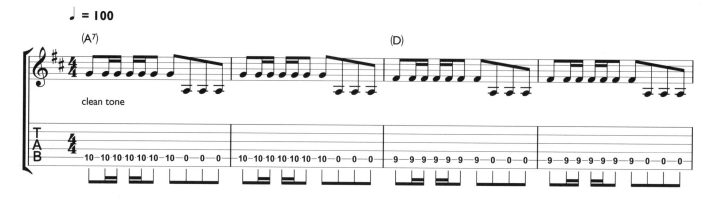

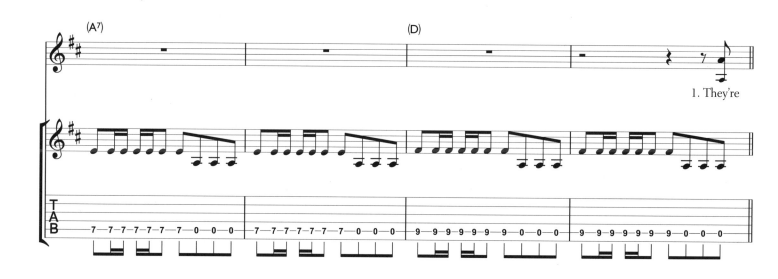

(1.) pa - cing Pic - ca - dil - ly in packs___ a - gain,   and

(2.) man on the door___ has a head___ like Mars,   like a

WARNER/CHAPPELL MUSIC PUBLISHING LTD, LONDON W6 8BS

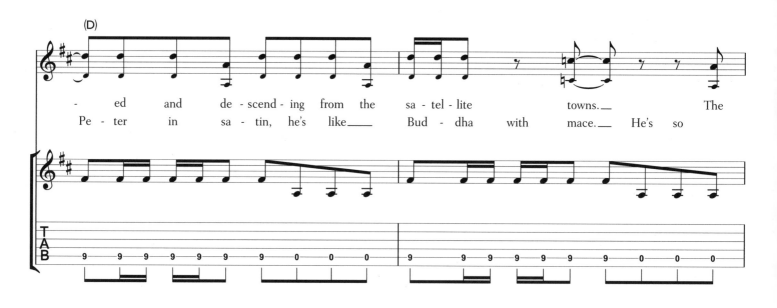

-ed and de-scend-ing from the sa-tel-lite towns.__ The
Pe - ter in sa - tin, he's like__ Bud - dha with mace.__ He's so

ne - on is graf-fi-ti sing-ing make a new start, so I look__
mer-ci-ful-ly free__ of the pres-sures of grace. Saint

for a plot where I can bu-ry my bro-ken heart.
Pe - ter in sa - tin, he's like__ Bud - dha with mace.__

I HEARD IT THROUGH THE GRAPEVINE

WORDS AND MUSIC BY NORMAN WHITFIELD AND BARRETT STRONG

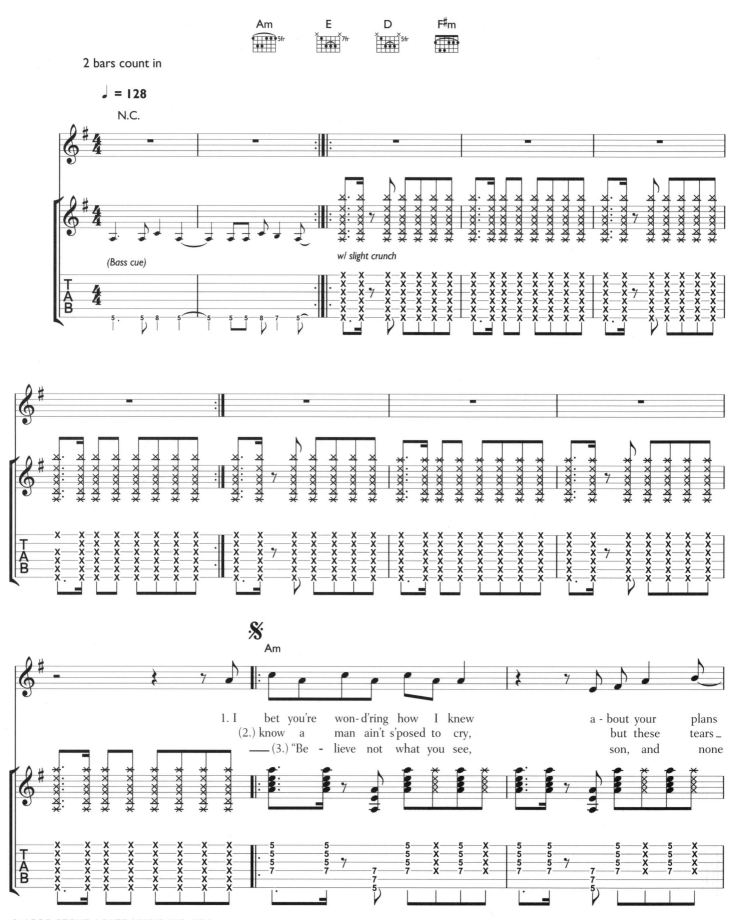

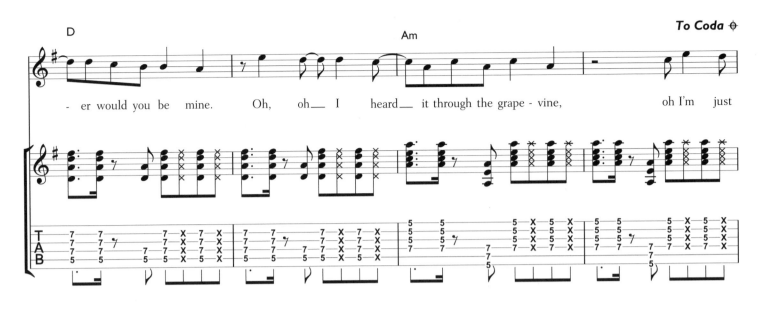

- er would you be mine. Oh, oh___ I heard___ it through the grape - vine, oh I'm just

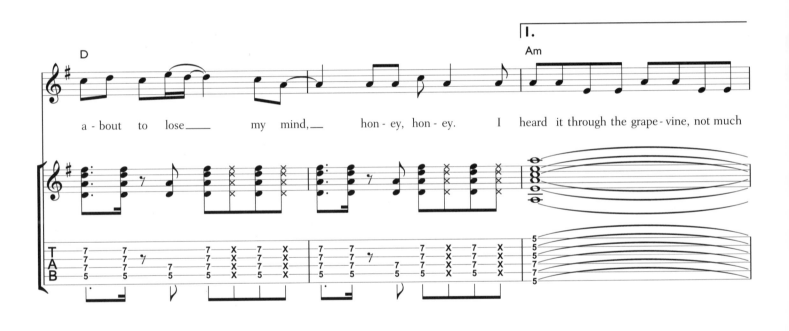

a - bout to lose____ my mind,___ hon - ey, hon - ey. I heard it through the grape - vine, not much

long - er would you be my ba - by.

2. I

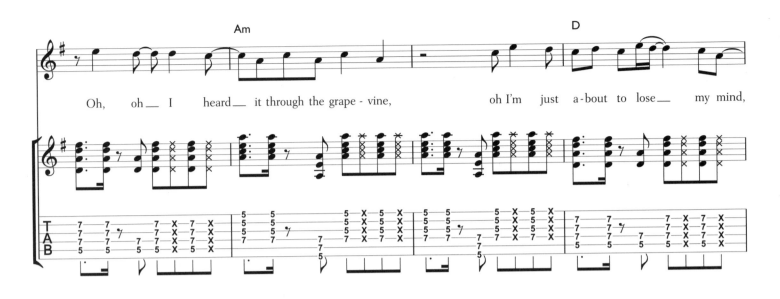

Oh, oh— I heard— it through the grape-vine, oh I'm just a-bout to lose— my mind,

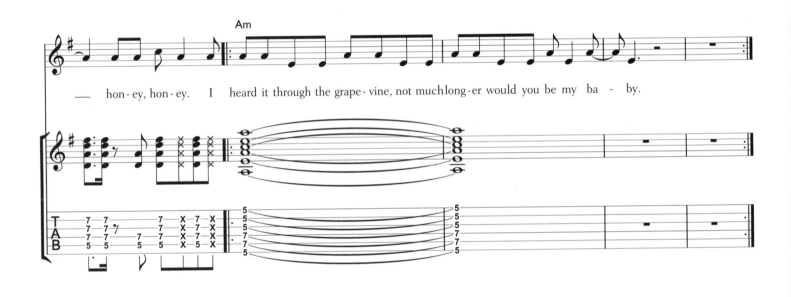

— hon-ey, hon-ey. I heard it through the grape-vine, not much long-er would you be my ba — by.

D.%̸ al Coda

3. Peo-ple say

(Synth. Bass cue)

w/ dist.

JUST FRIENDS

WORDS AND MUSIC BY JAMES GALLEY, SAMUEL FORREST, DAVID JONES AND MARTIN COHEN

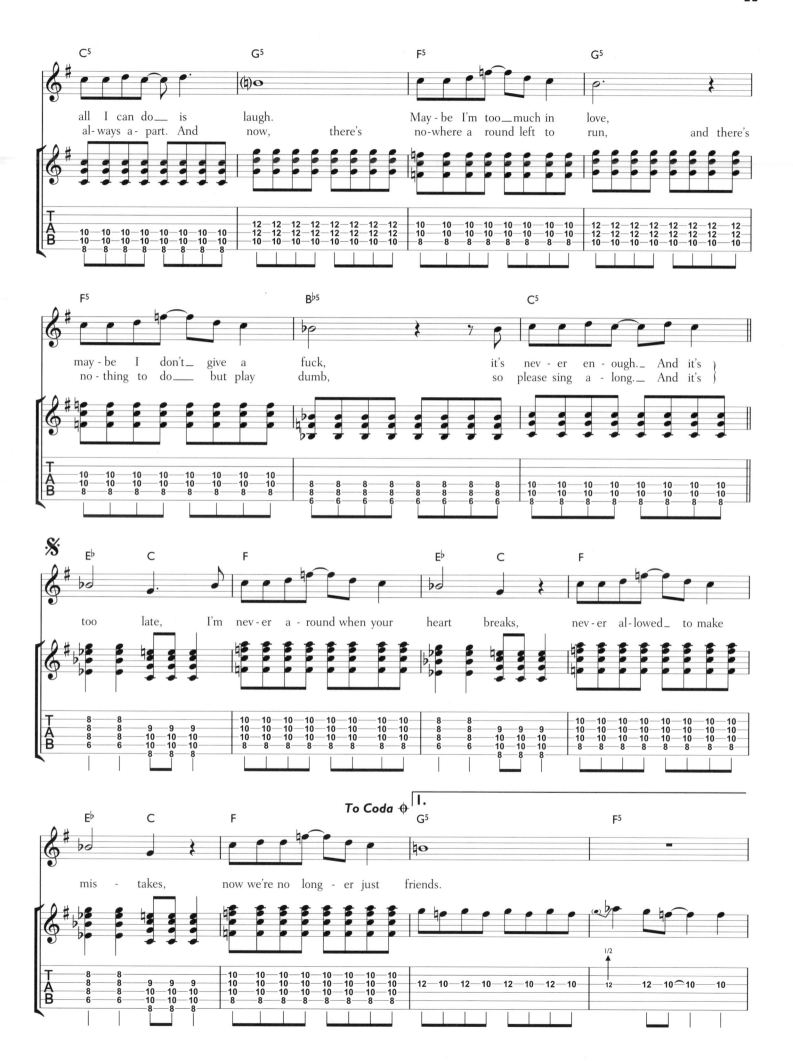

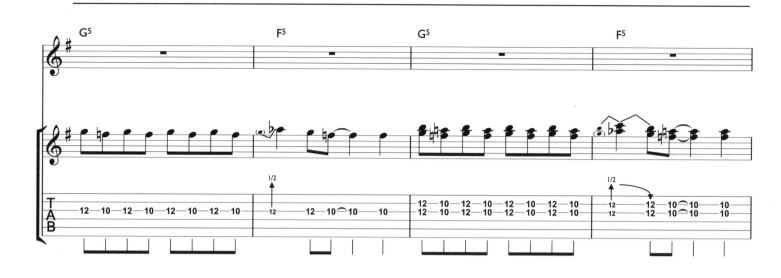

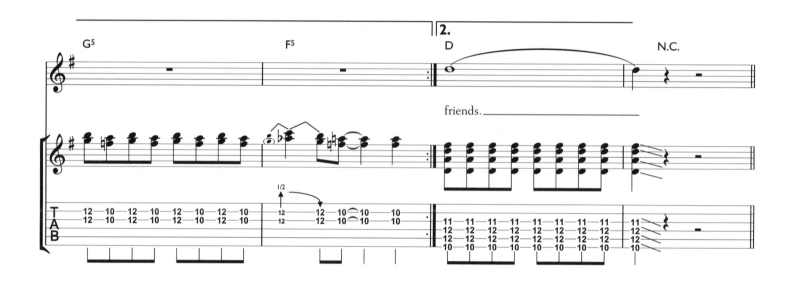

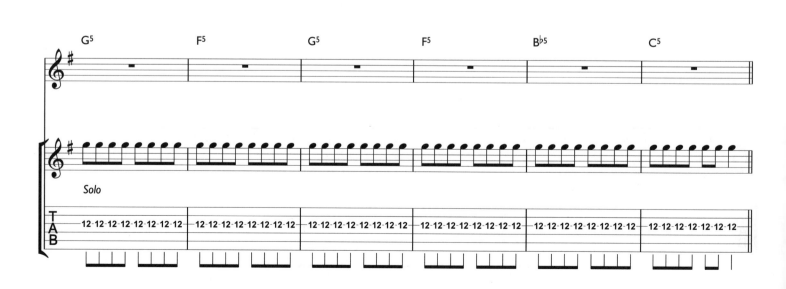

D.%. al Coda

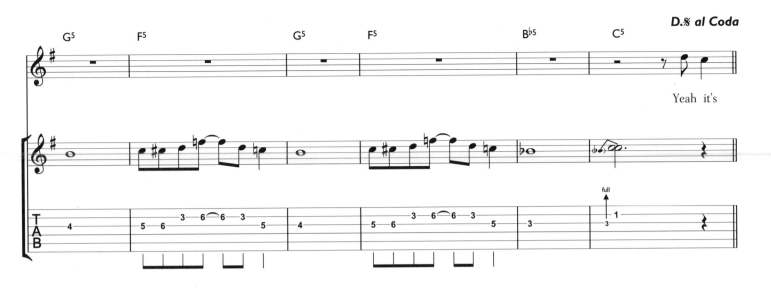

⊕ Coda

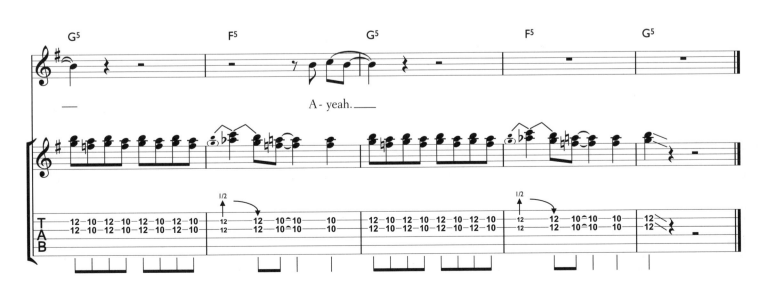

LIKE EATING GLASS

WORDS AND MUSIC BY KELE OKEREKE, RUSSELL LISSACK, GORDON MOAKES AND MATT TONG

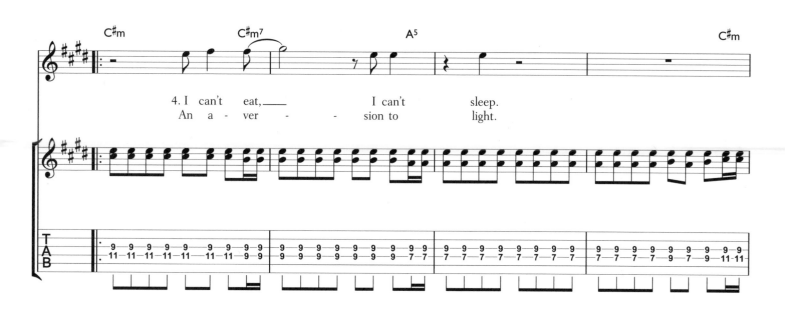

4. I can't eat,___ I can't sleep.
An a - ver - - - sion to light.

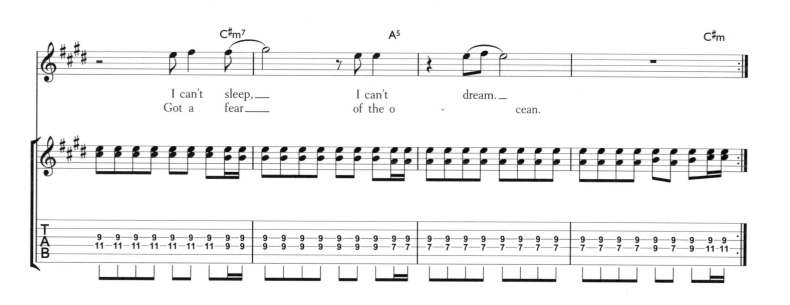

I can't sleep,___ I can't dream.___
Got a fear___ of the o - cean.

Like drink - ing poi - son,___ like eat - ing

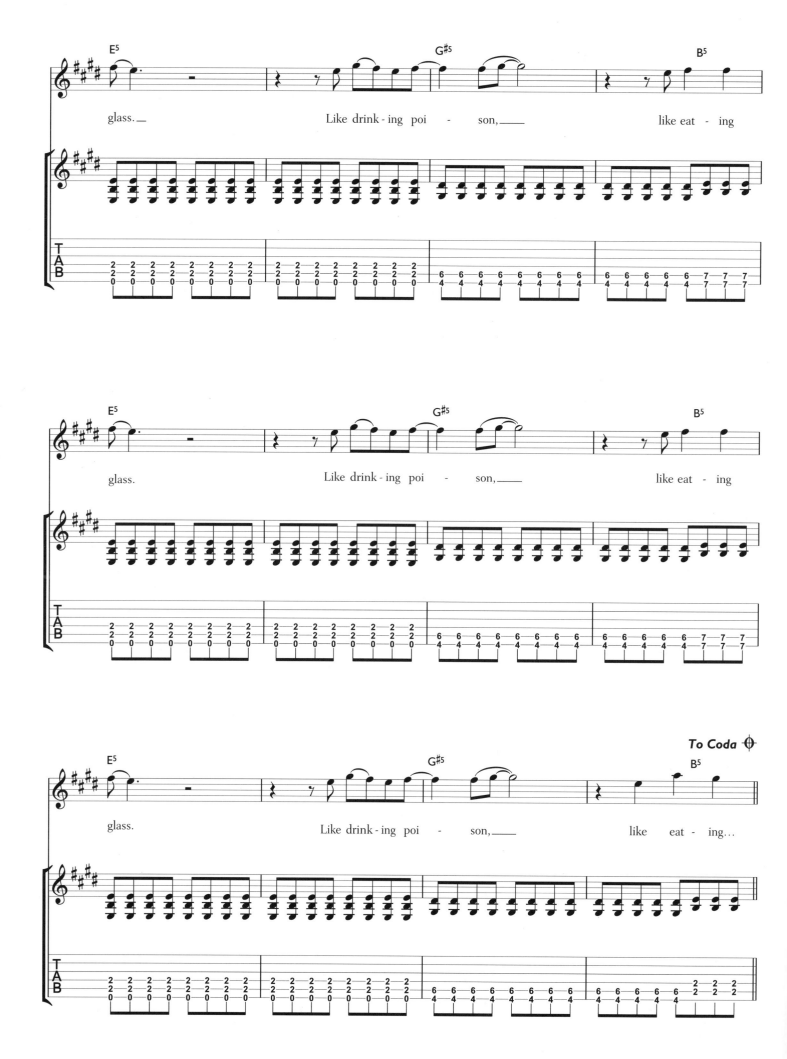

glass.___ Like drink-ing poi - son,___ like eat - ing

glass. Like drink-ing poi - son,___ like eat - ing

glass. Like drink-ing poi - son,___ like eat - ing...

To Coda ⊕

LOVE ME LIKE YOU

WORDS AND MUSIC BY ROMEO STODART

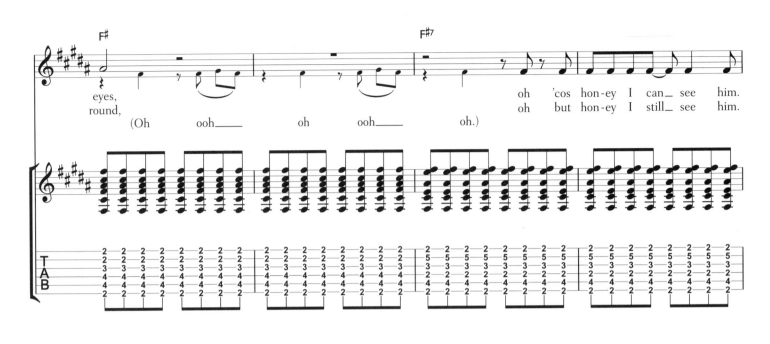

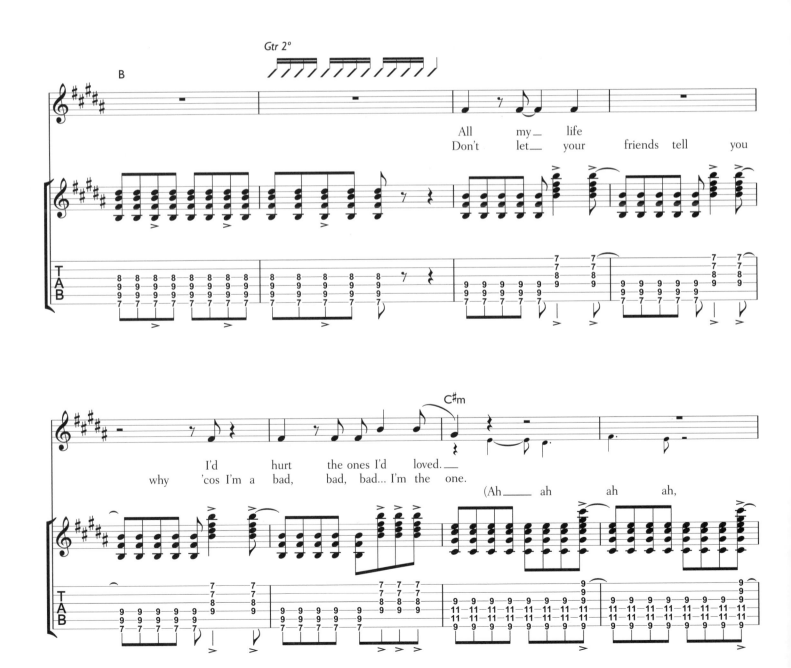

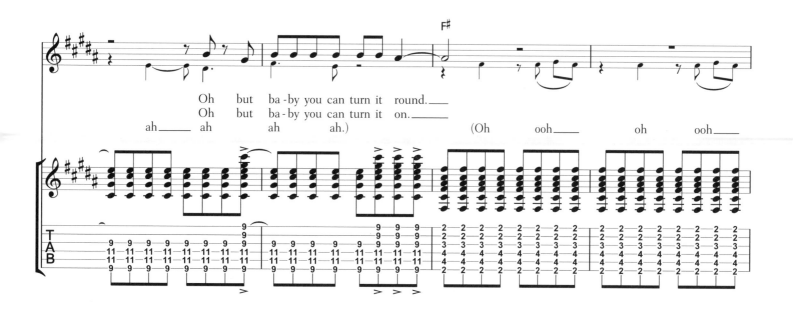

Oh but ba-by you can turn it round.____
Oh but ba-by you can turn it on._____
ah____ ah   ah   ah.)   (Oh   ooh____   oh   ooh____

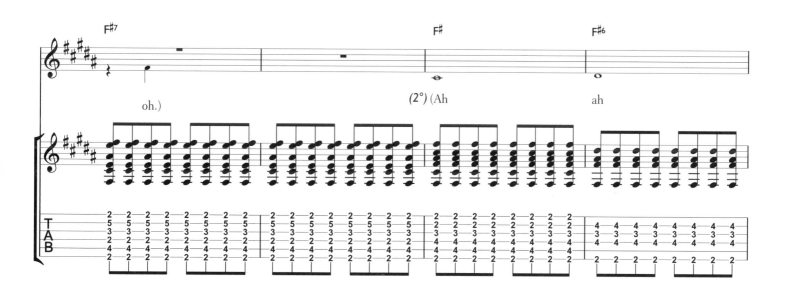

oh.)   (2°) (Ah   ah

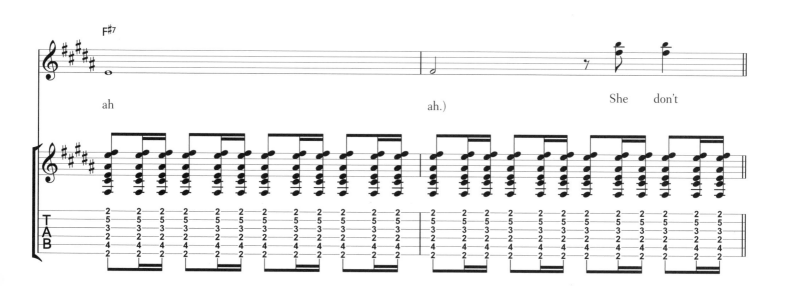

ah   ah.)   She don't

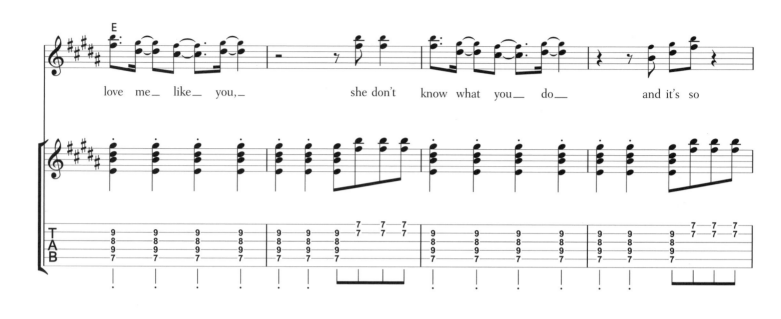

love me_ like_ you,_   she don't know what you_ do_   and it's so

hard._
(Ah ah____ ah ah____ ah.)   She don't

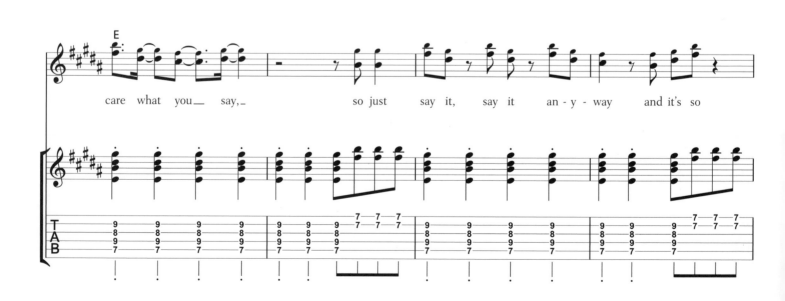

care what you_ say,_   so just say it, say it an-y-way   and it's so

find a way to make it hard_ for you.__ You'll

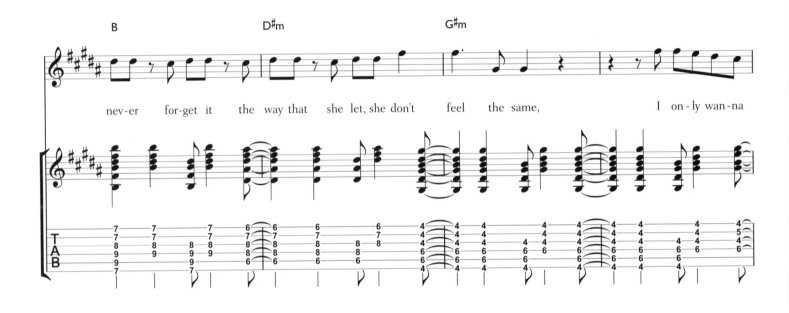

nev-er for-get it the way that she let, she don't feel the same, I on-ly wan-na

find a way to make it hard_ for you.__ She'll (Don't

nev - er for-get it the way that she let, she don't feel the same, I on-ly wan - na
fail me now, don't fail me now, don't fail me now, don't fail me now, don't

find a way to make it hard for you. She'll
fail me now, don't fail me now, don't fail me now, don't fail me now.) (Don't

ne-ver for-get it the way that she let, you don't feel no pain, I on-ly wan - na
fail me now, don't fail me now, don't fail me now, don't fail me now, don't fail

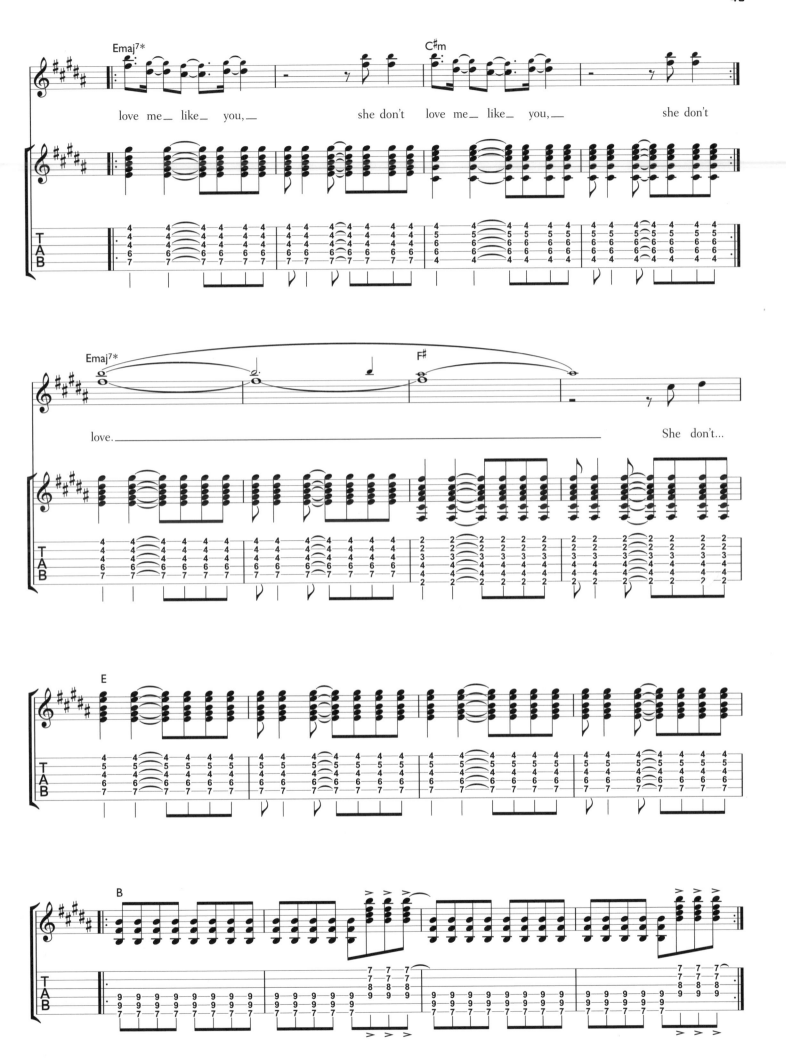

SNOWDEN

WORDS AND MUSIC BY JIMI GOODWIN, JEZ WILLIAMS AND ANDY WILLIAMS

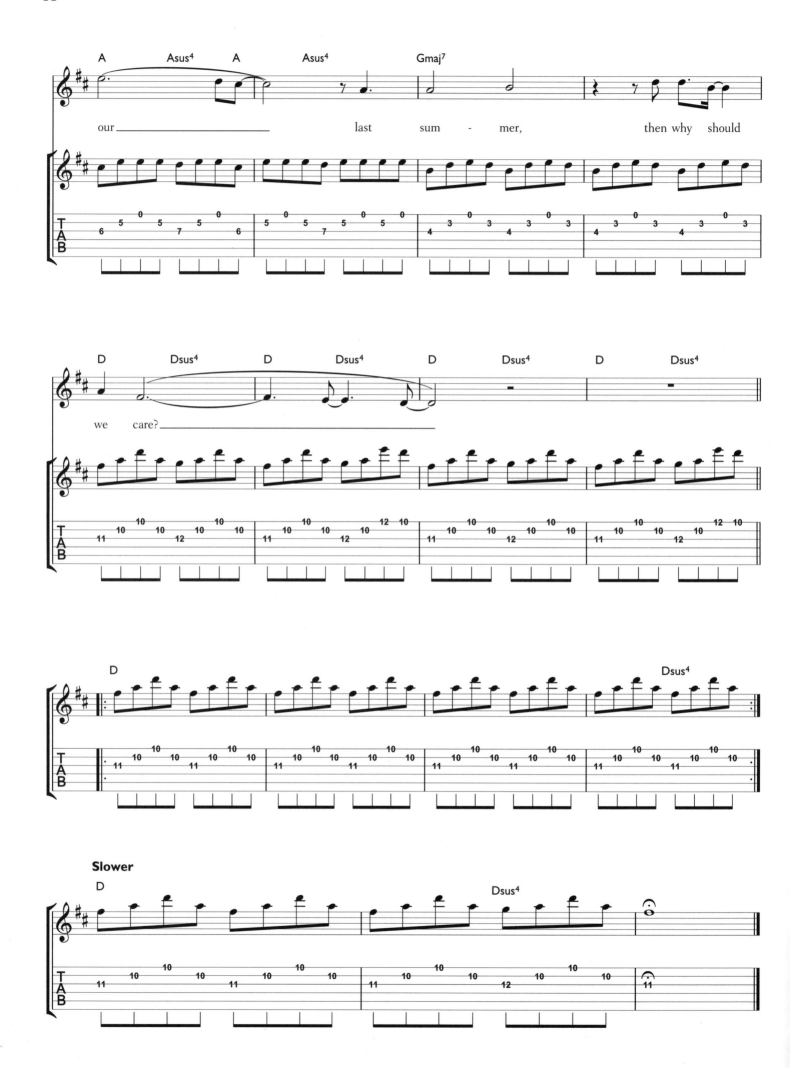

THIS TOWN AIN'T BIG ENOUGH FOR THE BOTH OF US

WORDS AND MUSIC BY RONALD MAEL

Zoo time is she and you time, the mam-mals are your fav-'rite type and you want her to-night.

Heart-beat, in-creas-ing heart-beat, you hear the thun-der of stam-ped-ing rhi-nos, el - e-phants and tack-y ti-gers.

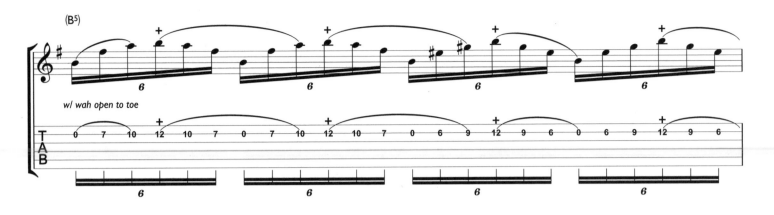

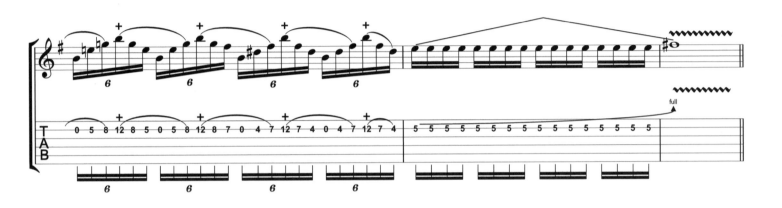

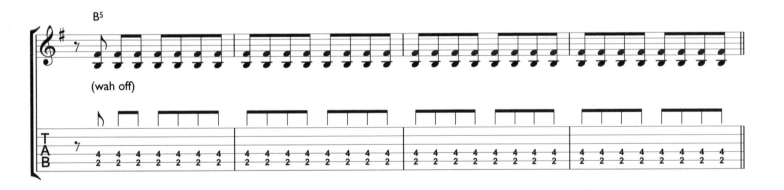

Show-er, an-oth-er show-er, you've got to look the best for her and be clean ev - 'ry - where.

Heart-beat, in-creas-ing heart-beat, the rain is pour-ing on the for-eign town, the bul-lets can-not cut you down.

This town ain't big e - nough for the both of us, but it ain't me who's gon - na

leave.

Cen-sus, the lat-est cen-sus, there'll be more girls who live in town, though not enough to go 'round.

Heart-beat, in-creas-ing heart-beat, you know that this town is-n't big e-nough, not big e-nough for both of us.

This town is-n't big e-nough, not big e-nough for both of us, I ain't gon-na leave!

(GONG)

WAKE ME UP WHEN SEPTEMBER ENDS

WORDS AND MUSIC BY BILLIE JOE ARMSTRONG, MICHAEL PRITCHARD AND FRANK E. WRIGHT III

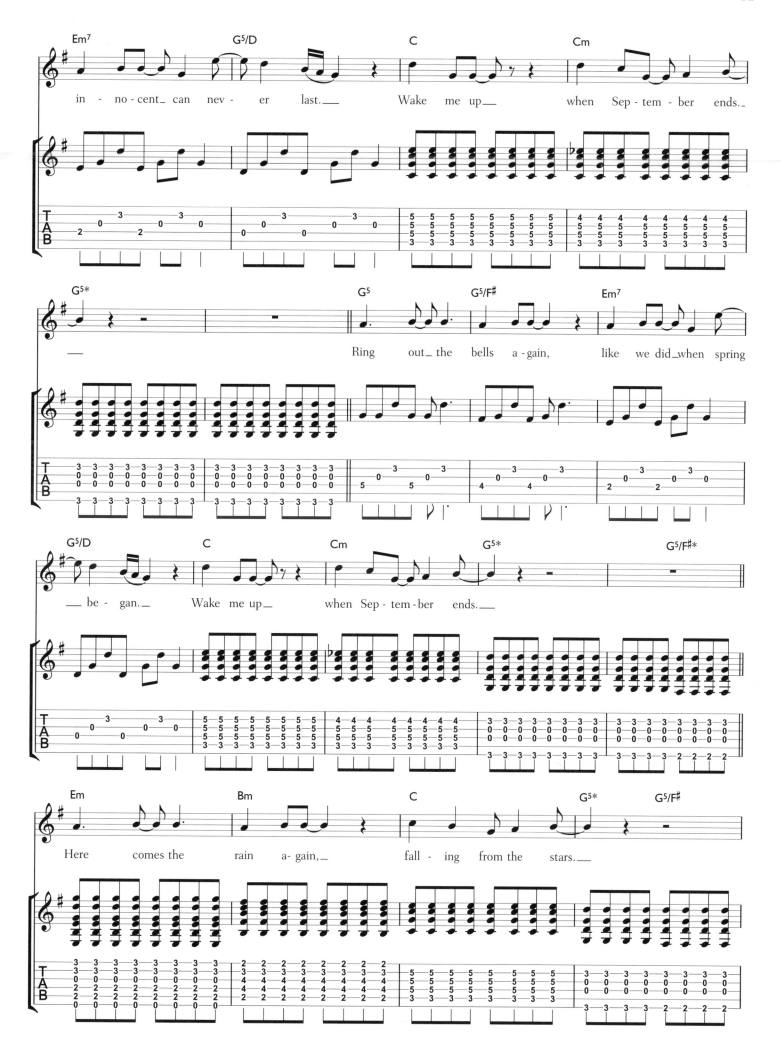

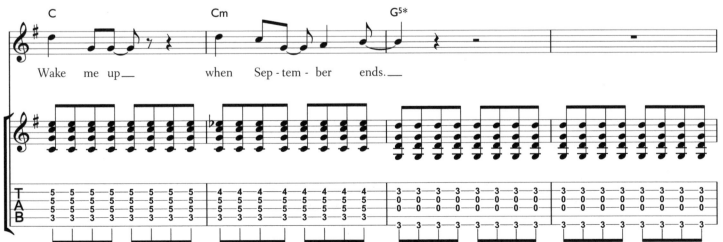

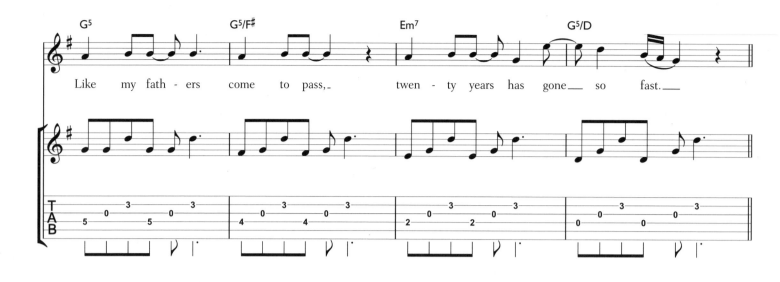

Like my fath - ers come to pass,___ twen - ty years has gone___ so fast.___

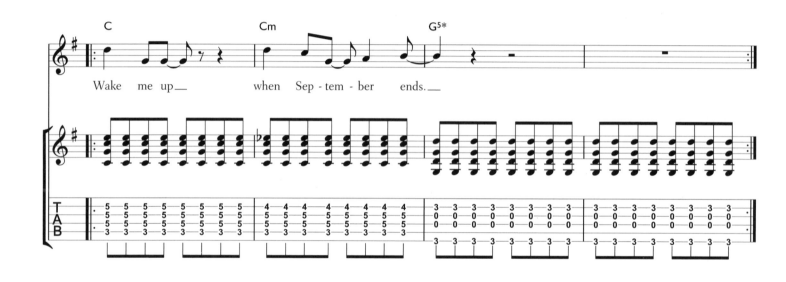

Wake me up___ when Sep - tem - ber ends.___

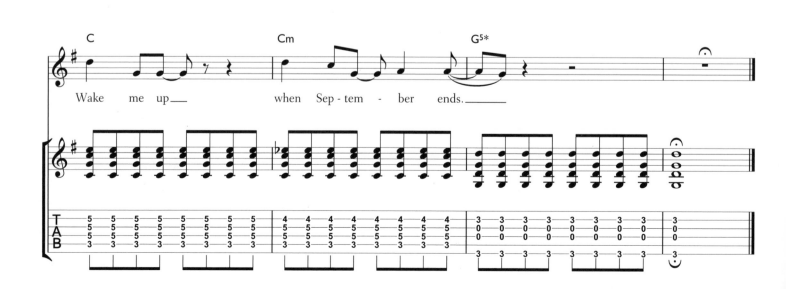

Wake me up___ when Sep - tem - ber ends._____